This book belongs to

....

This edition first published in 2018 by Alligator Products Ltd
Cupcake is an imprint of Alligator Products Ltd,
2nd Floor, 314 Regents Park Road, London, N3 2JX
www.alligatorbooks.co.uk

Written by Christine Swift
Illustrated by Claire Stimpson

Printed in China.0847

Calm Down, Billy!

Written by Christine Swift
Illustrated by Claire Stimpson

Billy Brontosaurus was a happy dinosaur, he got very excited about EVERYTHING!

"Do you want to play football?"
asked T-Rex

"Oh yesssss!"
replied Billy, excitedly.

T-Rex organised the teams.
"**Billy, you are on my team,**" he said.

Diplodocus, Stegosaurus and
Ankylosaurus come to join the game.

They used vines to make nets
between the trees.

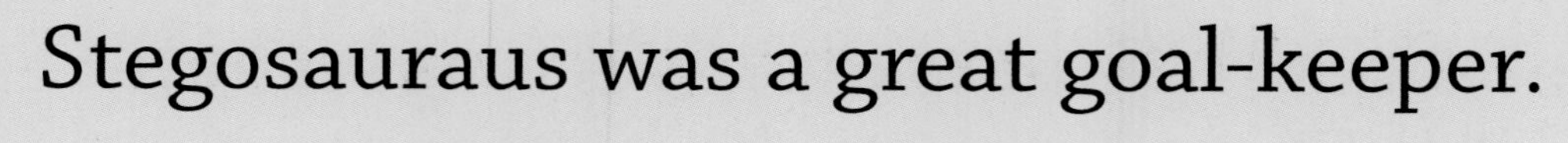

Stegosauraus was a great goal-keeper.

Pteradactyl squawked as T-Rex kicked the ball.

Billy came rushing in. He was so excited that he crashed straight into T-Rex!

"**Calm down, Billy**" shouted all the dinosaurs. "**You need to wait for your turn.**"

"**I'm sorry**", said Billy,
"**I was excited to be playing**".

Stegasauraus took a goal kick.

The ball went flying through the air.
In rushed Billy, again!

Billy charged in so quickly that he couldn’t stop, and crashed into the goal!

"I'm sorry" said Billy.

"**We are ALL excited**", said T-Rex,
"**but we have to play as a team, Billy**".

“**OK**”, said Billy, “**I will be more patient**”.

T-Rex kicked the ball, and Diplodocus passed it to Billy.

When the ball came towards him,
Billy kicked the ball.

Stesgosaurus dived, but Billy scored!
"**GOAL!**" they cheered.

"**Well done Billy**", the other dinosaurs congratulated him.

Billy felt very proud of himself.

"Next time you must be captain, Billy",

said T-Rex.

Billy was looking forward to next time!